# Self-Discovery Program Workbook

Nemadia B. Knuckles

0

Self-Discovery Program Workbook


Nemadia B. Knuckles

Philadelphia, PA

2

# Acknowledgment

To my family! My dad for his comedic sense of humor and love. My bonus mom for being so strong and my role model. My little sister Nectar, for her whimsical personality, courage, and understanding. My baby sister Naarah, for her strength and independence. My oldest brother Marcus for his love and forgiveness. For my oldest sister Remzee her fight to be stronger every day. My big brother Zubula for his resilience and love for life. My little brother R.L for his devotion to what he loves most. My niece Asha, for her honesty and encouragement. My big brother Anthony and big sister Shawnda, you are so amazing and kind. My biological mom, you tried your best, and that's all I could ask for. To all of my nieces and nephews, you are amazing!

To my friends. Shanice Jenkins, Latoya Perry, Nicole Boyd, Paige Black, Evelyn Pittman, Davia Dally, and Boimah Moiyallah. Thank you for helping in your own way.

# Table of Contents

# Preface

"Knowledge is power" is a complete understatement when it comes to understanding who you are in this world and finding your way through it. Nothing can be done about life being hard, but what can be done is choosing how we react to the difficult circumstances that come into our lives. Knowledge only takes us so far before we must embody wisdom. This workbook is intended to assist you in discovering this wisdom through acquiring a set of skills to utilize through different trials and tribulations, providing you with Peace Under Pressure.

**Finding self-discovery from within**

The Peace Under Pressure workbook may help you understand the reasons why you have made certain decisions in your life. With the help of life coaching, success coach, therapy, financial education, yoga, sexual health education and our activities program with Miss Goody Goody Desserts, you will be on your way to acquiring the knowledge to self-discovery. While on your way to realizing how you have been led and have led yourself on the path to where you are now, you face the opportunity to decide what you are going to do to improve your everyday actions towards a better outcome. This newly acquired knowledge is intended to help you come to the humbling realization that once you have an understanding of why you have made certain decisions in your life, that you can also make the decision to move beyond that which has caused you hardship and towards moments of accomplishment.

With this newly acquired knowledge, you will work smarter, gain determination, learn discernment and consistency and become intentional with personal decisions, personal finances, and your own knowledge and wisdom to live the life you want and have earned.

The newly acquired knowledge is to...

- ❖ **Forgive yourself of guilt and shame. Stop punishing yourself because you feel you don't deserve more. It is not the situation alone that brings about guilt or shame, but also how you respond to it.**
- ❖ **Mind your business. Tend to yourself and your surroundings, and the success of your personal business will follow suit.**
- ❖ **Understand your finances, spending habits, and passive income. Understand wealth, savings, and investments.**
- ❖ **Focus on all-around personal growth while being intentional in everything that you do.**
- ❖ **Be receptive to new information and having the discernment to know if and when it applies to you.**

A part of acquiring this knowledge is focusing on what brings you joy and makes you feel positive despite what has occurred in your life, keeping in mind that it is healthy and safe. Instead of allowing your difficult circumstances to define and destroy you, manifest your true self through the burning desire to accomplish more, through understanding what your goals and aspirations in life are. At Peace Under Pressure, Corporation. we have combined several different aspects of this process speaking to the mind, body, and soul simultaneously. We call it our self- discovery program. We offer this program with the intent to guide you in discovering your true self, your strength, and your ability to do all things that are humanly possible specific to your creative thoughts and skills acquired while in the Peace Under Pressure self-discovery program. It is our goal to build a network throughout the greater Philadelphia area and surrounding cities and states to establish an empire of purpose-driven women.

How do you not let your circumstances define or destroy you? But Instead, manifest into your true self through the burning desire to accomplish more. You do this through the understanding of knowing what your goals are, what your aspirations in life are, and knowing any other future accomplishments you would like to achieve.

You are the condition to your happiness; anything or anyone else that comes into your life should be a great addition and not the reason for your happiness. Our organization wants you to realize that you have a gift. Peace Under Pressure nonprofit Corporation

. considers a "gift" a set of skills developed or discovered by seeking knowledge and understanding. Everybody has a gift to be discovered and realized and in this space, we encourage you to allow it to blossom and give back and help as many people as possible.

**Know that it is not just the situation that happened that brings about guilt or shame, but how you respond to it.** You will one day manifest knowing how to free yourself from mental bondage and be able to live freely. To one day be able to move towards a lifetime of perfecting that craft, and to one day teach that craft to others, strengthening yourself and your newly acquired knowledge, is a beautiful moment and it begins right here.

# Telling Your Story

Telling your story is an essential part of your healing process. Every time you get to tell your story, you discover a new aspect of what you went through. These new discoveries provide you with self-awareness, which builds your strength and brings you closer to forgiveness.

Your story can be told in a variety of ways. It can be written in a journal or in a book, told to a close friend, or an audience. Take the time to explore the ways that are most impactful for you and best enable to you learn and heal from your experience.

This sharing process encourages you to hear and connect with the details that have brought you into the place that you are currently in.

The nuanced aspects of your situation are lessons to learn from. Once you begin to come into these lessons, you become empowered to establish what you will go on to tolerate from others and from yourself.

Forgive yourself for what has happened. You cannot be carrying the burdens of what has happened to you. It was only a lesson that you can now say, you've learned from. At the time in question, you may not have known better, you might have been scared, you might have felt alone, you might have been financially bound, you might have even felt that you deserved it, or couldn't do any better.

If we look at the knowledge that was gained from our situation, we might be able to say it was because we were uninformed. But now, we know better, so will do better, so make the decision that you will not carry this burden with you. Make the choice to free yourself, do not punishing yourself for things done in your past, it will only be a catalyst for making the same mistakes in your future.

We hope that telling your story enables you to forgive yourself for what has happened. Part of sharing your experience is being kind to yourself. In building your self-awareness and strength, we want you to make the choice to free yourself from your past.

# Introduction

Peace Under Pressure is a safe place to tell your story. Record your story. Write it down. However you choose to do it, let your story be told, so that you may start your healing process. After writing it, discard the story if you desire. Or share it at the next meeting. This process will not be easy. You are here to peel off layers of your old self while building up the new you. At times you may feel angry, embarrassed, or scared. You may even feel unintelligent. Learning comes with humility.

You are not alone with these feelings. Here we will face our fears, our failures, and what some might perceive to be defects. As you will learn in your membership with Peace Under Pressure, our life experiences are lessons, a series of lessons that we now know present the opportunity for us to become better versions of ourselves. Every member has had a moment in time when they may have felt that they were just a lump of coal. But remember, diamonds are formed in the earth's mantle from three crucial ingredients: Pressure, Heat, and Time.

When organizing Peace Under Pressure, my hope was to create fellowship amongst members. It is encouraged that we share our stories and build a community so that we may all be able to grow, learn, develop, and strengthen our character, allowing us to work in our purpose.

Sharing our experiences will create a tight-knit community. Nothing says we have to personally go through a particular experience to learn from it. Sharing can help members find lessons in what others have gone through.

Confidentiality is a must. What is said in our community, will stay in our community.

We must be mindful to speak the truth concerning our fellow members and still treat each other with dignity and respect.

"One key to courtesy is to understand where people are coming from. Discover their history. When you know what they've been through, you will be more understanding. Instead of thinking about how far they still must go, think about how far they have come in spite of their hurts." Rick Warren - *The Purpose Driven Life*[1]

This workbook was created for people to be open and honest with themselves about how they feel about themselves and their current state of mind. One cannot become the change they wish to become if they are not open and honest about who they are and why they became that way. I want all members to grow from what has happened to them. This is not about forgetting about the past; it is about learning from the past. This will be an ongoing process. As long as you are alive you will always be learning and growing. You will be triumphant! Say it out loud, and more importantly, believe it!

"Welcome to Peace Under Pressure. Turning Tragedy into Triumph."

# Nemadia B. Knuckles

## What You Will Need to Complete This Workbook

1.    A notebook

2.    A writing utensil

3.    1-2 hours a day

4.    Honesty

5.    Dedication

6.    Attendance at Peace Under Pressure Events and Meetings

7.    Active involvement in personal hobbies, interests, and community-based activities

# Two Wolves - A Cherokee Parable

An old Cherokee is teaching his grandson about life:

"A fight is going on inside me," he said to the boy.

"It is a terrible fight and it is between two wolves. One is evil—

he is anger, envy, sorrow, regret, greed, arrogance, self-pity,

guilt, resentment, inferiority, lies, false pride, superiority, and

ego." He continued, "The other is good—he is joy, peace, love,

hope, serenity, humility, kindness, benevolence, empathy,

generosity, truth, compassion, and faith. The same fight is going

on inside you—and inside every other person, too." The

grandson thought about it for a minute and then asked his

grandfather: "Which wolf will win?" The old Cherokee simply

replied, "The one you feed.[2]"

-Billy Graham

# Let's Measure Your Self-Esteem

Date: _____

On a scale from 0 to 5, with 0 being not at all and 5 being very much, rate how you currently feel in the following categories.

Confident

0        1        2        3        4        5

Happy

0        1        2        3        4        5

Sad

0        1        2        3        4        5

Disgusted

0        1        2        3        4        5

Overwhelmed

0        1        2        3        4        5

Alone

0       1       2       3       4       5

Loved

0       1       2       3       4       5

Liked

0       1       2       3       4       5

Attractive

0       1       2       3       4       5

Date: _____

Who are you? How do you describe yourself? In the columns below, fill in both the positive and negative sides. Which side has more?

| Positive Traits (I see in myself) | Negative Traits (I see in myself) |
|---|---|
|  |  |
|  |  |
|  |  |
|  |  |
|  |  |
|  |  |
|  |  |
|  |  |
|  |  |
|  |  |
|  |  |
|  |  |
|  |  |
|  |  |

Date: _____

The list below consists of positive personality traits. Circle the traits that you have; place a star next to the traits that you would like to have.

| | | | | | |
|---|---|---|---|---|---|
| Accountable | Adaptable | Adventurous | Affectionate | Alert | Ambitious |
| Appropriate | Assertive | Astute | Attentive | Authentic | Aware |
| Braves | Calm | Candid | Capable | Certain | Charismatic |
| Collaborative | Committed | Communicator | Compassionate | Connected | Considerate |
| Consistent | Cooperative | Courageous | Creative | Curious | Dedicated |
| Determine | Diplomatic | Direct | Disciplined | Easygoing | Effective |
| Efficient | Empathetic | Empowered | Energetic | Enthusiastic | Ethical |
| Excited | Expressive | Fair | Faithful | Fearless | Flexible |
| Friendly | Generous | Grateful | Happy | Hard-Working | Honest |
| Honorable | Humorous | Imaginative | Immaculate | Independent | Innovative |
| Inquiring | Integrity | Intelligent | Intentional | Interested | Joyful |
| Knowledgeable | Listener | Lively | Logical | Loving | Loyal |
| Manages Time Well | Networker | Nurturing | Open-Minded | Optimistic | Organized |
| Patient | Peaceful | Planner | Playful | Poised | Polite |
| Powerful | Practical | Presents Self | Proactive | Problem- | Productive |

| | | Well | | Solver | |
|---|---|---|---|---|---|
| Punctual | Reliable | Resourceful | Responsible | Self-Confident | Self- Reliant |
| Sensual | Serves Others | Sincere | Skillful | Spiritual | Spontaneous |
| Stable | Strong | Successful | Supportive | Tactful | Trusting |
| Trustworthy | Trustful | Versatile | Vibrant | Warm | Willing |
| Wise | Zealous | | | | |

Date: _____

**Automatic and Negative Thoughts Vs Affirmations**

In the first column, write down every negative thought you think others think about you and that you think of yourself. In the second column, write down the opposite of each thought you wrote in the first column. The second column will serve as your positive affirmations to recite daily. For example: column 1 "No one likes me" column 2 "People like me."

| Automatic and Negative Thoughts (Column 1) | Positive Affirmations (Column 2) |
|---|---|
|  |  |
|  |  |
|  |  |
|  |  |
|  |  |
|  |  |
|  |  |
|  |  |
|  |  |

|  |  |
|---|---|
|  |  |
|  |  |
|  |  |
|  |  |
|  |  |
|  |  |
|  |  |
|  |  |
|  |  |
|  |  |
|  |  |
|  |  |
|  |  |
|  |  |
|  |  |
|  |  |
|  |  |
|  |  |
|  |  |

Date: _____

In order to stop the negative thoughts that feed low self-esteem, it's important to know what triggers the thoughts. What happens right before you begin to feel bad about yourself?

_____

_____

_____

_____

_____

_____

_____

_____

_____

_____

_____

Date: _____


Your actions are a result of your thoughts and beliefs.  What are some of the things that you have done (both positive and negative) as a result of the beliefs and thoughts?

_____

_____

_____

_____

_____

_____

_____

_____

_____

_____

_____

_____

Date: _____

What consequences have your actions had on your self-esteem, life and overall happiness?  Were the actions worth the consequence?

_____

_____

_____

_____

_____

_____

_____

_____

_____

_____

_____

_____

Date: _____

Give yourself one compliment and write about the experience of how you felt giving yourself that compliment, list any difficulty you had, and all of the emotions you experienced.

_____

_____

_____

_____

_____

_____

_____

_____

_____

_____

_____

_____

_____

Date: _____

Who do you talk to when you are not having positive thoughts and/or feelings? Do you have a support system, friends or family members you can turn to? If so, write a journal entry about that person including (who he/she is, how you know them and why you trust them in your time of need.) If you do not have a person, write down the type of person you would like to talk to in your time of need.

_____

_____

_____

_____

_____

_____

_____

_____

_____

_____

_____

Date: _____

On a scale from 0 to 5 with 0 being not at all and 5 being very much; rate how you feel right now in the following categories. Have your scores changed? If so, describe the differences in this entry.

Confident

0        1        2        3        4        5

Happy

0        1        2        3        4        5

Sad

0        1        2        3        4        5

Disgusted

0        1        2        3        4        5

Overwhelmed

0        1        2        3        4        5

Alone

0        1        2        3        4        5

Loved

0      1      2      3      4      5

Liked

0      1      2      3      4      5

Attractive

0      1      2      3      4      5

# Part 1

Many who feel like they do not deserve more out of life tend to hold onto guilt and shame, later punishing themselves because they feel guilt or shame. Peace Under Pressure will help you understand how you deal with guilt and shame and what you should do when you feel them. Everyday actions that tend to bring us mental nourishment when done in moments associated with guilt and shame, might be used as self-inflicted punishment and can become destructive.

**1. When you feel guilt or shame, do you eat? Please explain.**
a. Are you eating to feel happy?
b. Are you eating because you're bored?
c. Are you eating because you feel lonely?
d. Are you eating to punish yourself?
e. Are you eating because you feel bad about yourself or feel sorry for yourself?

**2. When you feel guilt or shame, do you sleep? Please explain.**
a. Are you sleeping to avoiding your feelings?
b. Are you sleeping because you're bored?
c. Are you sleeping because you feel lonely?
d. Are you sleeping because you feel sorry for yourself?

**3. When you feel guilt or shame, do you shop? Please explain.**
a. Do you shop to feel happy?
b. Do you shop because you're bored?
c. Do you shop because you feel lonely?
d. Do you shop to fit in, or to impress people?

4. **When you feel guilt or shame, are you seeking companionship? Please explain.**
a. What kind of companionship do you tend to seek?
b. Are you trying to fill a void?
c. Are you not acknowledging the guilt or shame by substituting it with a person?
d. Are you feeling joy through/because of another person because you feel you cannot make yourself happy?
e. Do you seek companionship to feel good, because you're bored and believe you have nothing to work on or towards that is bringing you satisfaction and fulfillment?
f. Do you seek companionship because you feel lonely, or because you are looking for love and happiness from someone other than yourself?

5. **When you feel guilt or shame, are you having sex? Please explain.**
a. Sex is great and when had under the right circumstances can lead to great companionship with the right person.
b. If you are having sex for fun, being open and honest about that with yourself can help you make smarter decisions about whom you are having sex with and why.
   i. Are you having sex to feel loved?
   ii. Are you having sex to feel companionship?
   iii. Are you having sex to feel wanted?
   iv. Are you having sex because you feel insecure about your appearance, and having sex makes you feel attractive, and liked?
   v. Are you having sex to feel better about yourself?
   vi. Are you having sex because you're bored?
   vii. Are you having sex because you feel lonely?
a. If any of the 7 reasons apply to your decision making, when you feel guilt or shame, or feel the urge to punish yourself, It's best that you reconsider putting sex on hold for your safety, and the safety of others

6. **When you feel guilt or shame, do you seclude yourself? Please explain**

a. Secluding yourself can put you in a place where you are not aware of the world around you. Having full awareness of your surroundings puts you in a place to be in present time. Being in present time, will allow you to see what is available to you, by being inquisitive, and seeking answers so that you will have mental, emotional, and possible financial increase in your life.

7. **Do you no longer try new things? Do you no longer challenge yourself? Please explain.**

a. Not trying new things leaves you complacent and stifles your ability to know what you are, and what you are not good at. It can put you in a position to not do fun activities or projects. Not trying new things can have you not see new things by traveling the world, or trying new and exciting foods.

b. What new thing have you tried, or plan on trying?

8. **What do you do when you feel shame, do you eat?**

a. Food is amazing especially when cooked right. But when you eat because of shame or guilt, you might very well be eating your emotions, which can sometimes last for hours, days, weeks or years depending on if you can learn how to recognize when you are feeling shame or guilt. Thus, finding a way to stop yourself. With the necessary help from Peace Under Pressure self-discovery program, we can help you recognize this behavior.

9. **Do you not challenge yourself, when you feel shame? Please explain.**

a. Holding yourself to a new level is allowing yourself to not be complacent with how things are in your life. Having the desire to want more, is to create a thought in your mind that you might have to work harder, longer and more passionately to accomplish a desired task or project, or goal, to live the life you want.

## 10. Are you minding your business?

a. When having a mentor or when you look up to someone, it can have positive effects on minding someone else's business, only, and only when it comes to having a mentor.

b. But when you don't mind your business in a way that brings a negative outcome, such as caring too much about what others are thinking about you, or looking at what others are doing to see which of you has more, is significantly taking all of the time and energy you could use to focus on how you can be better, stronger, and wiser than you were yesterday.

## 11. Are you comparing yourself

a. Things that can happen when you compare yourself (Can make you feel), unworthy, guilty, ugly, not smart enough, inadequate, not good enough, not wealthy enough, prideful, jealous, defeated, and envious.

b. Spending time and energy focusing on things, people and objects can take away focus from building a mental, physical, spiritual, emotional, and financially stable environment for your personal life.

## 12. Focus on all-around personal growth while being intentional in everything that you do. Ask yourself questions like...

a. Do I understand my finances?

b. Do I understand how to have multiple streams of income?

c. Do I understand mutual funds, budgeting, whole life insurance, real estate, stocks & bonds?

d. Am I being intentional in everything that I do?

e. Do I have self-control over how I am responding to this situation?

f. Am I settling?

g. Am I genuinely happy?

h. Am I being strategic?

i. Am I being flexible?

Note: Focus on what brings you joy and what makes you feel positive despite what has occurred in your life, keeping in mind that those things are healthy and safe. Instead of allowing your difficult circumstances to define and destroy you, manifest your true self through the burning desire to accomplish more, through understanding what your goals and aspirations in life are. At Peace Under Pressure, Corporation. we have combined several different aspects of this process speaking to the mind, body, and soul simultaneously. We call it our self- discovery program. **Be receptive to new information and having the discernment to know when it applies to you.** We offer this program with the intent to guide you in discovering your true self, your strength, and your ability to do all things that are humanly possible and specific to your creative thoughts and skills acquired while in the Peace Under Pressure self-discovery program. It is our goal to build a network throughout the greater Philadelphia area and surrounding cities and states to establish an empire of purpose-driven women.

Note: How do you not let your circumstances define or destroy you? But Instead, manifest into your true self through the burning desire to accomplish more. Through the understanding of what your goals are, what your aspirations in life are, and any future accomplishments you would like to achieve.

Note: Why is this Information Important? because you are the condition to your happiness; anything or anyone else that comes into your life should be a great addition and not the reason for your happiness. Our organization wants you to realize that you have a gift. "A Gift" when referring to Peace Under Pressure, Corporation. is considered a set of skills developed or discovered by seeking knowledge and understanding. Everybody has "A Gift" to be discovered and realized and in this space we encourage you to allow it to blossom, so that you will one day be able to give back and help as many people as possible.

**Know that it is not just the situation that happened that brings about guilt or shame, but how you respond to it.** You will one day manifest the ability of knowing how to free yourself from mental bondage and be able to live freely. To one day be able to move towards a lifetime of perfecting that craft, and to one day teach that craft to others, strengthening yourself and your newly acquired knowledge, is a beautiful moment and it begins right here.

# Let's Measure Your Self-Esteem

Date: _____

On a scale from 0 to 5, with 0 being not at all and 5 being very much, rate how you currently feel in the following categories.

Confident

0     1     2     3     4     5

Happy

0     1     2     3     4     5

Sad

0     1     2     3     4     5

Disgusted

0     1     2     3     4     5

Overwhelmed

0     1     2     3     4     5

Alone

0      1      2      3      4      5

Loved

0      1      2      3      4      5

Liked

0      1      2      3      4      5

Attractive

0      1      2      3      4      5

# Week 2: When You Feel

## Part 2

1.  When you feel guilt or shame, do you eat? Please explain.

   _____

   _____

   _____

   _____

   _____

   _____

   _____

a.  Are you eating to feel happy?

   _____

   _____

   _____

   _____

_____

_____

_____

_____

_____

_____

b.     Are you eating because you're bored?

_____

_____

_____

_____

_____

_____

_____

_____

_____

c. Are you eating because you feel lonely?

_____

_____

_____

_____

_____

_____

_____

_____

_____

_____

d. Are you eating to punish yourself?

_____

_____

_____

_____

_____

_____

_____

_____

_____

_____

_____

e.    Are you eating because you feel bad about yourself or feel sorry for yourself?

_____

_____

_____

_____

_____

_____

_____

_____

_____

_____

_____

2. When you feel guilt or shame, do you sleep? Please explain.

_____

_____

_____

_____

_____

_____

_____

_____

_____

_____

_____

_____

_____

a.      Are you sleeping to avoiding your feelings?

_____

_____

_____

_____

_____

_____

_____

_____

b.      Are you sleeping because you're bored?

_____

_____

_____

_____

_____

_____

_____

_____

_____

_____

c.      Are you sleeping because you feel lonely?

_____

_____

_____

_____

_____

_____

_____

_____

_____

_____

d.     Are you sleeping because you feel sorry for yourself?

_____

_____

_____

_____

_____

_____

_____

_____

_____

3.   When you feel guilt or shame, do you shop? Please explain.

_____

_____

_____

_____

_____

_____

_____

_____

_____

a.      Do you shop to feel happy?

_____

_____

_____

_____

_____

_____

_____

_____

_____

_____

_____

b.   Do you shop because you're bored?

_____

_____

_____

_____

_____

_____

_____

_____

_____

c.   Do you shop because you feel lonely?

_____

_____

_____

_____

_____

_____

_____

_____

_____

_____

_____

_____

d.    Do you shop to fit in, or to impress people?

_____

_____

_____

_____

_____

_____

_____

_____

4.  When you feel guilt or shame, are you seeking
    companionship? Please explain.

    _____

    _____

    _____

    _____

    _____

    _____

    _____

    _____


a.  What kind of companionship do you tend to seek?

    _____

    _____

    _____

    _____

    _____

    _____

_____

_____

_____

_____

_____

b.      Are you trying to fill a void?

_____

_____

_____

_____

_____

_____

_____

_____

_____

_____

_____

c.   Are you not acknowledging the guilt or shame by substituting it with a person?

_____

_____

_____

_____

_____

_____

_____

_____

_____

d.   Are you feeling joy through another person because you feel you cannot make yourself happy?

_____

_____

_____

_____

_____

_____

_____

_____

_____

_____

_____

e.    Do you seek companionship to feel good, because you're bored and believe you have nothing to work on or towards that is bringing you satisfaction and fulfillment?

_____

_____

_____

_____

_____

_____

_____

_____

_____

_____


f.    Do you seek companionship because you feel lonely, or because you are looking for love and happiness from someone other than yourself?

_____

_____

_____

_____

_____

_____

_____

_____

_____

_____

_____

_____

5. When you feel guilt or shame, are you having sex? Please explain.

_____

_____

_____

_____

_____

_____

_____

_____

a. Are you having sex to feel loved?

_____

_____

_____

_____

_____

_____

_____

_____

_____

_____

_____

b.      Are you having sex to feel companionship?

_____

_____

_____

_____

_____

_____

_____

_____

_____

_____

_____

c.  Are you having sex to feel wanted?

_____

_____

_____

_____

_____

_____

_____

_____

_____

_____

d.  Are you having sex because you feel insecure about your
    appearance?

_____

_____

_____

_____

_____

_____

_____

_____

_____

_____

_____

e.    Are you having sex to feel better about yourself?

_____

_____

_____

_____

_____

_____

_____

_____

_____

_____

f.    Are you having sex because you're bored?

_____

_____

_____

_____

_____

_____

_____

_____

_____

_____

_____

_____

g.     Are you having sex because you feel lonely?

_____

_____

_____

_____

_____

_____

_____

_____

_____

_____

_____

Note: (If a through g) are reasons that apply to your decision making, when you feel guilt or shame, or feel the urge to punish yourself, It's best that you consider putting sex on hold for your safety, and the safety of others.

6. When you feel guilt or shame, do you seclude yourself? Please explain.

_____

_____

_____

_____

_____

_____

_____

_____

_____

_____

_____

_____

Note: Secluding yourself can put you in a place where you are not aware of the world around you. Having full awareness of your surroundings puts you in a place to be in present time. Being in present time, will allow you to see what is available to you, by being inquisitive, and seeking answers so that you will have mental, emotional, and possible financial increase in your life.

7. Do you no longer try new things? Please explain.

_____

_____

_____

_____

_____

_____

_____

_____

_____

_____

Note: Trying new things can open the door for enhanced experiences. Enhanced experience can drive creative thought, pushing the limits to your imagination.

8. Do you no longer challenge yourself? Please explain.

_____

_____

_____

_____

_____

_____

_____

_____

_____

_____

_____

_____

_____

Note: Challenging yourself can make you want to do and be better every day, leading to more completed task and bigger goals.

# More or Less

Numerous things can keep us from living the life that we want, the life we know belongs to us because we deserve it. So then, why don't we have that life? First, let us start with the most important question: Do we honestly feel we deserve it?

I say this is the most important question because many times I have found that people, including myself, are preventing their own prosperity. How? Simple. We often continuously punish ourselves for the things that have happened in our past. We have somehow convinced ourselves that the life we have always dreamed to be ours, cannot be ours at all.

Why might we be punishing ourselves exactly, why don't we feel we deserve it? Well, those questions depend on the individual to whom it is being addressed. At this time, I can only speak from my own perspective. I guess it's time to be a little vulnerable. I had no idea I was punishing myself until my ex-husband and I separated, May 18, 2018, and even after that, it had been several months until I finally came to that conclusion. What I specifically did to come to that conclusion, I will include in another blog post, but it was the most exciting journey I could have ever taken for myself, and I'm excited to say that I am currently on this journey and intend on staying on this journey until I am called to rest in peace.

I would like to start with how frequently I held on to a grudge. So very often, I held on to things people said to me and about me. I felt as if I was living to be angry and on guard. I disliked my stepmother, I thought my father could have been a better father, I was angry at my birth mother for abandoning me. I stopped talking to one of my older sisters, as well as my brother and his daughter. To be honest, I am not sure how much love I had for myself if any at all. I was just angry and full of misery.

One would never know that about me, ask anyone from high school or college, I was always smiling and wanting to be around people. But deep down inside, I was telling myself that I might not be able to obtain happiness and I treated myself accordingly. Once in the place, I stopped treating myself nicely. I never purchased nice items for myself, I never took a walk, went to a nice restaurant, or read a book at a park on a sunny day. I was a walking, talking, living, breathing human being wandering haphazardly. "For as a man thinketh in his heart, so is he." Proverbs 23:7.

I have discovered that when you don't have an expectation for yourself, you don't want or desire more. You settle, you expect the minimum and do the minimum. This same low energy is expected from the people you allow in your life.

I had to go through many trials and tribulations to come to the point where I love, appreciate, and respect myself. It is a journey that I have come to love. The things I have gone through in my life have led me to this exact path. This path has allowed me to share my experience with so many. I am honored and blessed to be a part of helping anyone who feels Peace Under Pressure will do for them what it has done for me.

# Let's Measure Your Self-Esteem

Date: _____

On a scale from 0 to 5, with 0 being not at all and 5 being very much, rate how you currently feel in the following categories.

Confident

0          1          2          3          4          5

Happy

0          1          2          3          4          5

Sad

0          1          2          3          4          5

Disgusted

0          1          2          3          4          5

Overwhelmed

0          1          2          3          4          5

Alone

0        1        2        3        4        5

Loved

0        1        2        3        4        5

Liked

0        1        2        3        4        5

Attractive

0        1        2        3        4        5

# Week 3: Getting Started

1. Do you have a support system?

_____

_____

_____

_____

_____

_____

_____

_____

a.    When was the last time you kept the company of women who were going through a situation similar to yours?

_____

_____

_____

_____

_____

_____

_____

_____

_____

_____

b.    How often did you meet?

_____

_____

_____

_____

_____

_____

_____

_____

_____

_____

c.  Did it help you? If so, how? If not, why not?

_____

_____

_____

_____

_____

_____

_____

_____

_____

NOTE: Make sure the people in your inner circle are here to encourage you and believe all the positive things you believe about yourself.

2.  What do you hope to gain from Peace Under Pressure?

_____

_____

_____

_____

_____

_____

_____

_____

_____

_____

3.  The kind of treatment you *deserve* from people and the type of
    treatment you *expect* from people are two different things. It is
    imperative that you know the difference between the two. Look
    up the definition of the two verbs, "deserve" and "expect" and
    write your definition of each here.

_____

_____

_____

_____

_____

_____

_____

_____

_____

_____

a.      What kind of treatment do you think you "deserve" from
        people?

_____

_____

_____

_____

_____

_____

_____

_____

_____

_____

b.       What kind of treatment do you "expect" from people?

_____

_____

_____

_____

_____

_____

_____

_____

c.       Why do you feel you "deserve" or "expect" to be treated that way? Please explain?

_____

_____

_____

_____

_____

_____

_____

_____


_____


_____


4. When was the last time you decided against your best interests to benefit someone else?

_____

_____

_____

_____

_____

_____

_____

_____

_____

_____

5. Self-control can be viewed as the opportunity to choose who you let control you. The best-case scenario is that you are controlling yourself, your actions, and how you react to things. When you are not the captain of your ship, you leave room for someone else to take control of you. Explain what being the captain of your ship means to you.

_____

_____

_____

_____

_____

_____

_____

_____

_____

a. Has someone ever attempted to take control of you? What was the situation?

_____

_____

_____

_____

_____

_____

_____

_____

_____

b.    Why do you think they were or were not able to gain control over you?

_____

_____

_____

_____

_____

_____

_____

_____

_____

_____

_____

c.   Why do you think you allowed it? If you did not allow it, how were you able to prevent it?

_____

_____

_____

_____

_____

_____

_____

_____

_____

_____

_____

d.   How will you make sure you are the only person in control of yourself?

_____

_____

_____

_____

_____

_____

_____

_____

_____

_____

_____

_____

_____

6. In the future if someone is trying to manipulate or control you, how do you make sure you stand in your beliefs on what is best for you?

_____

_____

_____

_____

_____

_____

_____

_____

_____

_____

_____

_____

_____

7.  Do you know the difference between someone with a
    controlling personality and someone who has constructive
    criticism? Explain your answer.

    _____

    _____

    _____

    _____

    _____

    _____

    _____

    _____

    _____

8.  What's an acronym for "self", in "self-control"? e.g.: (S) Self (E)
    Empowered (L) life (F) For me. What acronym do you think can
    work for you?

    _____

    _____

    _____

_____

_____

_____

_____

_____

_____

_____

_____

_____

9.  How well do you know your period symptoms of your menstrual cycle? Explain all your symptoms during your cycle.

_____

_____

_____

_____

_____

_____

_____

_____

_____

_____

Note: As I am going through my own process of rediscovering my character, I have been able to pay close attention to my body. I have discovered serious fatigue during the first two days of my period. I have also noticed a heightened emotional rollercoaster of feeling lonely, melancholy, and needy. I am aware of these symptoms; therefore, I am able to find alternative ways to effectively accomplish tasks at that time without feeling emotionally drained. Also, I am able to use my emotional intelligence to make decisions for myself when meeting new people.

10. What activities or processes are helpful in relieving your stress? Or help you think through or about the situation that is stressing you?

_____

_____

_____

_____

_____

# Let's Measure Your Self-Esteem

Date: _____

On a scale from 0 to 5, with 0 being not at all and 5 being very much, rate how you currently feel in the following categories.

Confident

0      1      2      3      4      5

Happy

0      1      2      3      4      5

Sad

0      1      2      3      4      5

Disgusted

0      1      2      3      4      5

Overwhelmed

0      1      2      3      4      5

Alone

0      1      2      3      4      5

Loved

0      1      2      3      4      5

Liked

0      1      2      3      4      5

Attractive

0      1      2      3      4      5

# Week 4: Where Did It Come From?

1.  Why do you think you allowed yourself to be in a situation that was unhealthy for you? What prevented you from leaving sooner rather than later? Please explain.

    _____

    _____

    _____

    _____

    _____

    _____

    _____

    _____

    _____

a.  Was it a habit? Did you find yourself dating the same person with a different face?

    _____

    _____

    _____

_____

_____

_____

_____

_____

_____

_____

b.    Was it loneliness? Were you feeling insecure? Did you believe you couldn't find anyone who would treat you better, love you better, support you emotionally or financially better?

_____

_____

_____

_____

_____

_____

_____

_____

_____

_____

_____

c.     Did you feel like you deserved whatever treatment was being given to you? Was the idea of marriage and/or having a partner more appealing to you than being single again and having to "start all over"?

_____

_____

_____

_____

_____

_____

_____

_____

_____

d.   Did you feel like losing your marriage would have been embarrassing to you and or your family? Were you worried about what people would say?

_____

_____

_____

_____

_____

_____

_____

e.   Did you rely upon your spouse for love and/or finance?

_____

_____

_____

_____

_____

_____

_____

_____

_____

_____

f.    Did you want to have a father for your children? Or have your children grow up in a two-parent household? Was that person someone you considered your only family?

_____

_____

_____

_____

_____

_____

_____

_____

_____

g.      Did you believe that no one could love you as they loved you?

_____

_____

_____

_____

_____

_____

_____

_____

_____

_____

_____

_____

_____

2. When was the last time you experienced love, joy, peace, and patience? Kindness, goodness, faithfulness, gentleness, and self-control? What was the situation, and how did it make you feel?

_____

_____

_____

_____

_____

_____

_____

_____

3. When was the last time you felt a sense of fear and hopelessness? What was the situation? And how often does this occur? Please answer in detail.

_____

_____

_____

_____

_____

_____

_____

_____

_____

_____


4. Why is patience important when getting to know someone new?

_____

_____

_____

_____

_____

_____

_____

_____

_____

_____

_____

_____

5. Do you feel like you are deserving of happiness? If so why or why not?

_____

_____

_____

_____

_____

_____

_____

_____

_____

_____

6. Are you afraid to start over? If so, please explain why or why not?

_____

_____

_____

_____

_____

_____

_____

_____

_____

7. Do you use vetting or discernment when meeting new people? If so, how has that helped you? If not, why? And how can vetting and discernment help you, moving forward?

_____

_____

_____

_____

_____

_____

_____

_____

_____

_____

Note: Discernment according to Webster's dictionary, is the ability to judge well.

Note: Learn to use discernment when meeting someone new. Be patient. Let that person show you who they are, their character, their motivation, and their aspirations in life. Make sure all of these qualities are action-oriented, and not just talk. Talk is cheap!

8. "Never regret being a good person to the wrong people. Your behavior says everything about you, and their behavior says everything about them." - Marc & Angel[3]. Please explain what this quote means to you, and how do you believe this can help you when it comes to meeting new people.

_____

_____

_____

_____

_____

_____

_____

_____

_____

9. What do you believe are your flaws or weaknesses? They can be internal or external.

_____

_____

_____

_____

_____

_____

_____

_____

_____

_____

_____

10. What flaws or weaknesses would you change about yourself?
    How would this make you a better person or change your life?

_____

_____

_____

_____

_____

_____

_____

_____

_____

_____

_____

_____

_____

_____

11. Consider keeping all your flaws and weaknesses. Describe how being aware of and acknowledging your flaws and weaknesses can be used to strengthen your character.

_____

_____

_____

_____

_____

_____

_____

_____

_____

_____

12. How can you use discernment for anyone who comes into your life while you are finding the strength to become stronger mentally, emotionally, and physically while at times feeling weak and flawed?

_____

_____

_____

_____

_____

_____

_____

_____

_____

_____

Note: I trust very easily. Because I have come to terms with this reality about myself, I now realize that I must take my time in giving people the best parts of myself before they deserve it. I give no more or no less than what I am shown or given, regardless of the situation.

# You vs Your mind

Positivity is a very crucial step in your healing process. In difficult times, negativity has the capacity to overshadow your light. We are here to encourage you to not let negative thoughts prevent you from reaching your fullest potential.

*All the flaws you feel that you have at how unintelligent you think you might be, or how you're are not creative. Those thoughts are asinine, far from the truth, and furthermore, they are preventing you from tapping into your best potential because they are taking up space in your mind that does not give way to creative thought.*

When your mind gives way to negative thoughts and feelings, that's just your mind playing tricks on you. It can lead you down a rabbit hole of feeling alone and often time like you're the only one with these negative thoughts and feelings. You are not alone! Everyone on earth, even successful people have feelings of doubt, fear, and inferiority. If you are not careful, if you allow yourself to believe those thoughts, you might start to seclude yourself, and have further thoughts that you are alone in those feelings, which couldn't be further from the truth.

Having a positive outlook begins with you. Feel empowered to be your biggest cheerleader and biggest fan. Having support from your family, friends, co-workers, and associates is valuable, but how you feel about yourself, comes from deep within. Though you may receive validations from others, you must believe them for yourself. Tell yourself that you are great, that you can have it all, that it can be yours, and most importantly, believe it.

# Let's Measure Your Self-Esteem

Date: _____

On a scale from 0 to 5, with 0 being not at all and 5 being very much, rate how you currently feel in the following categories.

Confident

0        1        2        3        4        5

Happy

0        1        2        3        4        5

Sad

0        1        2        3        4        5

Disgusted

0        1        2        3        4        5

Overwhelmed

0        1        2        3        4        5

Alone

0       1       2       3       4       5

Loved

0       1       2       3       4       5

Liked

0       1       2       3       4       5

Attractive

0       1       2       3       4       5

# Week 5: Turn It Around

1. How much of your past do you believe is in direct relation to your character today? Please be detailed.

_____

_____

_____

_____

_____

_____

_____

_____

_____

_____

a. Please describe the negative experience(s) that have contributed to shaping your character.

_____

_____

_____

_____

_____

_____

_____

_____

_____

_____

b.    Please explain the positive experience(s) that have contributed to shaping your character?

_____

_____

_____

_____

_____

_____

_____

_____

_____

_____

Note: What if all the negative and positive experiences in your life were not arbitrary? What if they happened because you needed to be strong for a later situation in your life that would have broken you mentally or emotionally if you had not gone through those earlier experiences? Or what if it was to help someone who might only survive their situation because of your personal experience? This is not to say you deserve what happened to you. This is only an alternative perspective on your circumstances.

2. How can you turn your tragedy into triumph to help you become a better and more productive person than you were yesterday? Or help other people become better and more productive?

_____

_____

_____

_____

_____

_____

_____

_____

_____


Note: My bonus mother was a disciplinarian. While I was growing up, she was, in my eyes, a typical stepmother. As a child, many nights I cried myself to sleep, wishing that my drug addicted biological mother would come and rescue me from my situation, a situation that I thought I could not live in. Fast forward to September 14, 2014. I married my ex-husband, who was verbally, emotionally, mentally, financially and at times physically abusive. When we separated on April 18, 2019, it was hard for me because I still wanted the marriage. However, I grew to forgive myself and find my purpose. On February 24, 2019, I called my bonus mother and thanked her for being such a strong and amazing person. Yes, she was a disciplinarian. However, she ingrained morals and values in me that have contributed to the woman I am today. She is a huge reason why I am so resilient. I believe she may be the reason I had the strength to stay alive in my marriage. I used to be angry with my bonus mother, and I used to hate my ex-husband, but I chose to interpret this as a gift of progress. My hurts during my childhood were real. The abuse that I endured during my marriage was real. But how I chose to handle it is also very real. "We all make mistakes, have struggles, and even regret things in our past. But you are not your mistakes, you are not your struggles, and you are here now with the power to shape your day and your future."- Steve Maraboli[4]

3. What guilt-driven memories are you allowing to dictate your future?

_____

_____

_____

_____

_____

_____

_____

_____

_____

c. Have you let a guilt-driven memory destroy a positive thing in your life because you feel defeated or unworthy?

_____

_____

_____

_____

_____

_____

_____

_____

_____

_____

d.    Are you punishing yourself because you believe you don't deserve a positive outcome in your life?

_____

_____

_____

_____

_____

_____

_____

_____

_____

e.   Will you make the decisions to rise above this? Please be
     detailed.

     _____

     _____

     _____

     _____

     _____

     _____

     _____

     _____

     _____

4.   So, you made a mistake. Yesterday, last week, two years ago...
     And I am sure you feel bad about it. What do your past mistakes
     have to do with today? Do you want to let it go? Not letting it
     go can increase the probability of it taunting you day after day,
     year after year. Please explain.

     _____

     _____

     _____

_____

_____

_____

_____

_____

_____

_____

5. What negative thoughts are boggling you down?

_____

_____

_____

_____

_____

_____

_____

_____

_____

_____

f.   What do you do when negative thoughts or feelings come about; telling you lies such as, you can't do it, or you're not smart enough?

_____

_____

_____

_____

_____

_____

_____

_____

g.   How do you handle hearing such false statements about yourself?

_____

_____

_____

_____

_____

_____

_____

_____

_____

_____

6. Have you had one bad event happen after another? Please be
   detailed.

_____

_____

_____

_____

_____

_____

_____

_____

h.    Do you feel you have no hope of things getting better, so why try?

_____

_____

_____

_____

_____

_____

_____

_____

_____

_____

_____

_____

_____

i.      What attitude do you have when you begin the day? Are you anxious? Are you sad, depressed?

_____

_____

_____

_____

_____

_____

_____

_____

_____

j.      Have you tried having a more positive attitude when starting your day? If so, what is your process to think more positively? If not, what is preventing you from thinking more positively?

_____

_____

_____

_____

_____

_____

_____

_____

_____

7.  Describe yourself. Who are you?

_____

_____

_____

_____

_____

_____

_____

_____

_____

k.    What do you like to do when you are not at work or taking care
      of your family?

      _____

      _____

      _____

      _____

      _____

      _____

      _____

      _____

l.    What do you enjoy about your life? Your job, your car, your
      family, your favorite season, etc.? Why?

      _____

      _____

      _____

      _____

      _____

_____

_____

_____

_____

8.  Are you ready to stop being a prisoner of your past? Are you
    ready for your past to be a lesson that you've learned from, to
    have a better present and future? Please explain why you feel
    you are ready to be free.

_____

_____

_____

_____

_____

_____

_____

_____

## Feeling Good

How do you feel? This is an important question to ask as you move towards living your best life and feeling good in the skin that you are in while you do it.

Feeling good can be a conscious decision. There are many ways to have a good time and place a smile on your face. Ask yourself what is on the agenda today, and do just that. Are you going to go for a walk, do your hair, take a long bath, go to the movies, cook a nice dinner, or hang out with friends? You are the most important person in your life, treat yourself as such.

*Placing yourself in moments and with people that make you feel good should be done both for the sake of mental health and for the pure enjoyment of living a happy, fulfilled life. If it's a safe and healthy way to make you smile, I say go for it, and put your best foot forward while doing so.*

In the process of enjoying your own life, you might be tempted to compare your journey to those of others. This is a recipe for disaster. If you do find that you are comparing yourself to others, rather than being inspired by them, shift your thoughts immediately and focus on what you can do and what you want to do better, personally. You are your own competition. Run your own race. When you become your own foundation, it is amazing how much joy you let in.

# Let's Measure Your Self-Esteem

Date: _____

On a scale from 0 to 5, with 0 being not at all and 5 being very much, rate how you currently feel in the following categories.

Confident

0      1      2      3      4      5

Happy

0      1      2      3      4      5

Sad

0      1      2      3      4      5

Disgusted

0      1      2      3      4      5

Overwhelmed

0      1      2      3      4      5

Alone

0       1       2       3       4       5

Loved

0       1       2       3       4       5

Liked

0       1       2       3       4       5

Attractive

0       1       2       3       4       5

# Week 6: Resentment

1. What happened in your past was not your fault. If you believe this to be so, explain why. If you believe this to be false, explain why.

_____

_____

_____

_____

_____

_____

_____

_____

2. Have you tried forgiving yourself for what occurred in your past? Please explain.

_____

_____

_____

_____

_____

_____

_____

_____

_____

_____

Eg: I realize now that I did not have boundaries in my marriage. I was willing to allow so many things to happen to me. I was so fixated on saving my marriage and avoiding the embarrassment it would cause me to have people know that my marriage failed. It was so bad. My ex-husband was able to convince me that the way he was treating me was because I did not love him enough. That I did not look at him the way he looked at me. That I was just so jealous. That these other women were his friends, and the reason he didn't like coming home or being around me was because I was so miserable and unhappy. When I did find out about the cheating and confronted him about the other women, he declared (with tears rolling down his cheeks and a snotty nose) it was because he could be himself around them. That they were more fun and livelier. That he was so sorry and got married too young. That he never wanted to hurt me, and he loved me so much and wanted this marriage to work. That I was his forever...

As time went on, he became sharper with his confessions of his cheating, down to how our intimate moments were unsatisfactory because my body was not connecting to his. That I did not give myself to him the way other women gave themselves to him. He would try to tell me that all I had to do was do better, love him more, and be more receptive to how he wanted me to be during intimacy. He even noticed that I was trying, and stated he was happy to see that I was willing to try harder to please him.

When we separated eventually, I longed for him. I wanted him to want to be with me. I was convinced that I was in love with my abuser, but the facts were, I was NOT in love with myself. Because I did not love myself I focused on wanting to prove to him that I was his one true love. I just needed one more chance to show him I loved him more than any of those other women did.

3. Why might you be in love with your abuser?

_____

_____

_____

_____

_____

_____

_____

_____

_____

_____

4. Are you internalizing your anger from the hurt that occurred in your past?

_____

_____

_____

_____

_____

_____

_____

_____

_____

_____

Note: What happened to you, was not your fault. Once you can grasp this concept, there are many things in your life that will be the same but will feel different. Going out with friends will feel somehow new and different. You will discover new places to go in your city you never noticed before. Food will taste even more delicious. You might even smile just because you're alive and well and happy.

5. What or who are you resenting from your past?

_____

_____

_____

_____

_____

_____

_____

_____

_____

_____

_____

_____

a.    Is holding on to resentment hurting you or the person you are holding the resentment towards? Explain your answer.

_____

_____

_____

_____

_____

_____

_____

_____

_____

_____

b.    What would it feel like to be able to let go of that resentment? Be detailed.

_____

_____

_____

_____

_____

_____

_____

_____

_____

_____

c.     Do you believe letting go of that resentment is going to be a positive or negative experience? Why?

_____

_____

_____

_____

_____

_____

_____

_____

_____

_____

_____

_____

_____

6. How many opportunities in your life have you missed out on because of fear?

_____

_____

_____

_____

_____

_____

_____

7. Are you afraid of failing?

_____

_____

_____

_____

_____

_____

_____

_____

a. Do you believe you are not good enough?

_____

_____

_____

_____

_____

_____

_____

_____

_____

_____

b.    Do you believe you don't deserve the life you could have if you wrote that book, made that invention, started that non profit, or opened that boutique?

_____

_____

_____

_____

_____

_____

_____

_____

_____

_____

c.      What experience from your past caused you to resist taking any chances?

_____

_____

_____

_____

_____

_____

_____

_____

_____

_____

_____

_____

_____

_____

d.    Do you think pursuing your dreams will require more work out of you? More than what you are currently doing to make a living right now? Please explain your answer.

_____

_____

_____

_____

_____

_____

_____

_____

_____

_____

e.  Is the financial freedom that you want or being debt-free not worth working hard?

_____

_____

_____

_____

_____

_____

_____

_____

Note: I have concluded that a lot of things are hard and so many things are annoying. Some things are not hard at all, but just tedious. For me, I would rather work on the tedious, annoying things that will give me mental, emotional and physical satisfaction. But everything else that is hard, annoying, and tedious does not offer me the same satisfaction. So, I put my efforts in things that will give me joy no matter how hard, tedious, or annoying it is.

8.  What happened in life that made you not take a great opportunity that was given to you? Please be clear regarding why you may have missed out on good opportunities in your life.

_____

_____

_____

_____

_____

_____

_____

_____

_____

9.  Coast vs. net worth. How many times have you purchased an item only because it made you feel good, or made you feel valuable? For example, purchasing an item because it made you feel good, compared to purchasing an item because it's going to benefit you? What insecurities, if any, were you trying to hide with retail therapy?

_____

_____

_____

_____

_____

_____

_____

_____

_____

10. What is preventing you from believing that you should have more in your life? This does not entail materialistic items, though it may be a driving force for some.

_____

_____

_____

_____

_____

_____

_____

_____

_____

_____

_____

11. What, if anything, do you believe you want or need in your life to make you happy?

_____

_____

_____

_____

_____

_____

_____

_____

_____

Note: Let them go. Sometimes people are in your life only to get what they can gain from you. Once they have taken everything they can, they are done with you. Let them go, they are wrong for you. They are blocking positivity from entering your life. Their absence leaves space for something good to come into your life.

# Let's Measure Your Self-Esteem

Date: _____

On a scale from 0 to 5, with 0 being not at all and 5 being very much, rate how you currently feel in the following categories.

Confident

0     1     2     3     4     5

Happy

0     1     2     3     4     5

Sad

0     1     2     3     4     5

Disgusted

0     1     2     3     4     5

Overwhelmed

0     1     2     3     4     5

Alone

0       1       2       3       4       5


Loved

0       1       2       3       4       5


Liked

0       1       2       3       4       5

Attractive

0       1       2       3       4       5

# Week 7: Time is of the Essence

1. How often do you seek the approval of others?

   _____

   _____

   _____

   _____

   _____

   _____

   _____

   _____

   _____

2. Are some of the choices you make in your life based on what others think? Be detailed with your answer.

   _____

   _____

   _____

_____

_____

_____

_____

_____

_____

_____

3. Is it very important to you to please others? Why or why not?

_____

_____

_____

_____

_____

_____

_____

_____

_____

_____

_____

4. Do you believe you are NOT capable of making an informed and intelligent decision about what you want out of your life? Why or why not?

_____

_____

_____

_____

_____

_____

_____

_____

_____

_____

_____

5. Time can never be repaid. To whom are you giving your time?

_____

_____

_____

_____

_____

_____

_____

_____

_____

a. What did they do or show you to prove they are deserving of your time, which can never be repaid?

_____

_____

_____

_____

_____

_____

_____

_____

_____

6.  Do you find yourself seeking the approval of others? Or believe
    what people say about you defines who you are?

_____

_____

_____

_____

_____

_____

_____

_____

_____

_____

_____

7. Does the approval of others give you an accomplished or satisfactory feeling that you are doing something right or increase your worth? Explain.

_____

_____

_____

_____

_____

_____

_____

_____

_____

_____

_____

_____

8. Do you seek the approval of others to make any of the decisions for your life? Having a child, going to school, getting a job, your sexual orientation or preference, etc.?

_____

_____

_____

_____

_____

_____

_____

_____

_____

_____

9. What thoughts come to mind when you do something or make a decision without the approval of others? Do you feel you are not smart enough, brave enough, skilled enough? Explain your

answer. From what experience in your life do you believe these thoughts or fears come?

_____

_____

_____

_____

_____

_____

_____

_____

_____

10. Challenge yourself to refrain from asking the opinions of others for a few days a week or even a month about a decision that you would like to make for yourself. Write down your goals. Track your progress with questions 10a -10d.

_____

_____

_____

_____

_____

_____

_____

_____

_____

_____

_____

_____

a.    Do you believe you can live up to this challenge?

_____

_____

_____

_____

_____

_____

_____

_____

_____

_____

b.     If so, how will you accomplish this challenge?

_____

_____

_____

_____

_____

_____

_____

_____

_____

c.     Is this a difficult challenge for you? Why or why not? Please be detailed.

_____

_____

_____

_____

_____

_____

_____

_____

_____

_____

d.     Please indicate if you succeed. If so, for how long?

_____

_____

_____

_____

_____

_____

# Let's Measure Your Self-Esteem

Date: _____

On a scale from 0 to 5, with 0 being not at all and 5 being very much, rate how you currently feel in the following categories.

Confident

0          1          2          3          4          5

Happy

0          1          2          3          4          5

Sad

0          1          2          3          4          5

Disgusted

0          1          2          3          4          5

Overwhelmed

0          1          2          3          4          5

Alone

0      1      2      3      4      5

Loved

0      1      2      3      4      5

Liked

0      1      2      3      4      5

Attractive

0      1      2      3      4      5

# Week 8: Claim it! It's Already Yours!

1.  If you could give your self-worth a value or a number, this far in the workbook, how would you measure it? What is that value or number? Why?

_____

_____

_____

_____

_____

_____

_____

_____

_____

_____

_____

2. Has anyone ever become upset with you because you cannot do what they request?

_____

_____

_____

_____

_____

_____

_____

_____

a. Does their request only benefit the requestor and not you?

_____

_____

_____

_____

_____

_____

_____

_____

_____

b.      Are you giving more to the relationship than you are receiving?

_____

_____

_____

_____

_____

_____

_____

_____

_____

_____

_____

3.  Who in your life gives you room to grow, learn, and make mistakes? Who supports you when you are wrong without criticizing you and making you feel bad about the new lesson you have learned?

_____

_____

_____

_____

_____

_____

_____

_____

_____

_____

4.  Why is it important to become uncomfortable with complacency for your character development?

_____

_____

_____

_____

_____

_____

_____

_____

5. List a few things in your life you are hoping for. Be as detailed and descriptive as possible.

_____

_____

_____

_____

_____

_____

_____

_____

_____

_____

_____

6. Keep your head high and demand from yourself a new way of thinking. Do more of what you want. Want more so that you never become complacent. Write down what you deserve.

_____

_____

_____

_____

_____

_____

_____

_____

_____

_____

_____

a.      Do you feel you deserve those things? why or why not?

_____

_____

_____

_____

_____

_____

_____

_____

b.      What else could you ask for that you feel you deserve and why?

_____

_____

_____

_____

_____

_____

_____

_____

_____

_____

_____

7. Was asking for more items difficult for you? Do you feel you
   don't deserve them? If so, why or why not? Explain in detail.

_____

_____

_____

_____

_____

_____

_____

_____

_____

_____

_____


8.  If you had all the money you could ever dream of for a day,
    what would your day look like? From the time you wake up, to
    the time you go to bed, what are the details of your day? It is
    very important that you are as detailed as possible. This
    includes your bedroom appearance, down to bed sheets. Where
    are you living? What does your place look like? What do you
    wear for the day? What do you do for a living to attain this
    lifestyle? Use another sheet of paper to complete your answer if
    necessary.


_____

_____

_____

_____

_____

_____

_____

9. How can you tell the difference between productivity and activity?

_____

_____

_____

_____

_____

_____

_____

_____

10. How do you ensure you use your time productively?

_____

_____

_____

_____

_____

_____

_____

_____

_____

11. Does your work/career feel meaningless to you?

_____

_____

_____

_____

_____

_____

_____

_____

_____

a.     If so, what would you rather be doing? What steps are you
       making to move towards it?

_____

_____

_____

_____

_____

_____

_____

_____

b.     If no action has been taken, explain why. If this job is
       meaningful to you, explain why.

_____

_____

_____

_____

_____

# Let's Measure Your Self-Esteem

Date: _____

On a scale from 0 to 5, with 0 being not at all and 5 being very much, rate how you currently feel in the following categories.

Confident

0     1     2     3     4     5

Happy

0     1     2     3     4     5

Sad

0     1     2     3     4     5

Disgusted

0     1     2     3     4     5

Overwhelmed

0     1     2     3     4     5

Alone

0      1      2      3      4      5

Loved

0      1      2      3      4      5

Liked

0      1      2      3      4      5

Attractive

0      1      2      3      4      5

# Week 9: Don't Worry. Be Happy.

1.  What would you do with your day if you had no other responsibilities to anyone but yourself? Why?

    _____

    _____

    _____

    _____

    _____

    _____

    _____

    _____

    a.  What would you buy, and why?

    _____

    _____

    _____

    _____

_____

_____

_____

_____

_____

_____

b.    Where would you travel, and why?

_____

_____

_____

_____

_____

_____

_____

_____

_____

_____

_____

_____

_____

_____

2. What has recently occurred in your life that has assisted with character development (changed you for the better) and helped you figure out what you can do in your life that makes you happy?

_____

_____

_____

_____

_____

_____

_____

_____

_____

a.      What is that thing that makes you happy?

_____

_____

_____

_____

_____

_____

_____

_____

_____

Note: Going through a divorce can be stressful, largely due to having to fight against the norm that as a woman, you are the reason your marriage ended. After my divorce I gained so much strength and my life gained new, powerful meaning. I knew I wanted to share that strength with other women.

3. It's always great to have friends and family by your side when there is a disappointment or when things are not going as planned. But, what can you do to encourage yourself in an unexpected event, disappointment, or when you're reminded of an event you wish never occurred?

_____

_____

_____

_____

_____

_____

_____

_____

4. What are some things you can do in the morning to make sure you start a brand-new day feeling joyful and full of life?

_____

_____

_____

_____

_____

_____

_____

_____

_____

_____

5.  We record things to watch it later, or to play it as many times as we like, whenever we like. Unfortunately, sometimes negative thoughts replay in our head the same way, like a recording from our past. What if you simply did not allow yourself to have time for that? Have you tried forcing a positive thought to push out the bad thoughts? You have had so many great things happen in your life. So many things have made you smile. What are some things that have brought some joy into your life that can help push out negative thoughts?

_____

_____

_____

_____

_____

_____

_____

_____

_____

_____

NOTE: There is a season for everything, a season to be happy, sad, mourn, and laugh. In the season of happiness and laughter, may it last as long as possible. However, in the season of sadness and mourning, it should not, and does not last forever. Do not be discouraged, and do not allow it to continue into another season. Take back your joy!

6. As the seasons come, the seasons also go. Don't be discouraged that business idea has not started yet or made its expected profit. Maybe it just hasn't been awakened in the right season and needs time to develop. What is a dream you have pursued that may have not been in its season just yet?

_____

_____

_____

_____

_____

_____

_____

_____

_____

7. Life happens. As we all know, things are thrown in our direction that may shift us from our positive feelings. What are some things we could recite and/or do (non-chemical) to help calm our nerves and the situation that we are going through, thus establishing peace under the pressures of life?

_____

_____

_____

_____

_____

_____

_____

_____

_____


8. If you can learn to be happy exactly where you are in your life today by looking at what's good in your life, then it is also possible that you can transition to be exactly where you think you are supposed to be in your life. Where do you think you are supposed to be, to be full of joy and have complete happiness?

_____

_____

_____

_____

_____

_____

_____

_____

_____

_____

9. If it is hard for you to think of this place of happiness, right now is the time to do so. What is blocking your happiness? It is important that you identify what it is. Figuring it out can be the start of your healing process, the development of growing stronger, both mentally and physically. This will all contribute to your character. What do you think might be stealing your joy?

_____

_____

_____

_____

_____

_____

_____

_____

_____

_____

_____

10. How do you believe you can take back your joy in a healthy way and have power over your life by changing the way you approach challenging situations?

_____

_____

_____

_____

_____

_____

_____

_____

_____

_____

_____

_____

_____

# Let's Measure Your Self-Esteem

Date: _____

On a scale from 0 to 5, with 0 being not at all and 5 being very much, rate how you currently feel in the following categories.

Confident

0        1        2        3        4        5

Happy

0        1        2        3        4        5

Sad

0        1        2        3        4        5

Disgusted

0        1        2        3        4        5

Overwhelmed

0        1        2        3        4        5

Alone

0      1      2      3      4      5

Loved

0      1      2      3      4      5

Liked

0      1      2      3      4      5

Attractive

0      1      2      3      4      5

# Week 10: Motivation Bowl

1. Are you the kind of person that is always seeing the bad, and somehow not able to see the good? Explain your answer

_____

_____

_____

_____

_____

_____

_____

_____

Note: This attitude can change. This is due to a mental shift that started occurring at a certain age in your life and took many years to master. It just requires another mental shift, to a more positive outlook for a change to occur. When an event occurs and your first thought is to be pessimistic, change the tone of it to something more positive. This will not happen overnight. It will take many years of lots of practice. And that's okay! It took time to develop that behavior (of negativity), so it will take time to change. Be patient with yourself. Anything good is worth fighting for.

2.  What are some things you like about yourself?

 

_____

_____

_____

_____

_____

_____

_____

_____

_____

_____

3.  What daily, weekly, or monthly hobby or activity could you pursue to help you figure out what brings enjoyment into your

life and leads you on the path to finding out your purpose?
Make a list. Use this list to help encourage you when necessary.

_____

_____

_____

_____

_____

_____

_____

_____

_____

_____

Note: MOTIVATION BOX-a physical box to keep in your home
with notes of encouragement. Once a day pick a note out and
read it out loud to yourself as a reminder of the great things
about yourself that can be referenced when encouragement is
needed.

4.  No one can treat you better than you treat yourself. Set the tone and the direction you would like your life to go in. When was the last time you treat yourself to a long walk, a movie, or a fancy dinner?

_____

_____

_____

_____

_____

_____

_____

_____

_____

Note: Are you taking steps towards finding what social activities mean the most to you? Finding out which activities you dislike is equally as important to finding your purpose. You can also love doing something and find it does not give you a sense of purpose, but maybe you like it because you get to share it with those you want to be around. I love rollerblading, but it does not give me purpose.

Note: Are you really who you say you are, or are you a different person depending on your circumstances and who surrounds you? If you have ever altered your personality depending on your situation, you should think about why you decided to take on a new personality. Were you uncomfortable? Did you feel insecure? Did you feel like you weren't good enough?

5.  When have you been 100% yourself?

_____

_____

_____

_____

_____

_____

_____

_____

_____

_____

a. "How did you feel?" "Do you feel this way often?" Where were you in that situation?

_____

_____

_____

_____

_____

_____

_____

_____

b. Who were you with and how do you feel about them? Are you happy with them? Sad or embarrassed?

_____

_____

_____

_____

_____

_____

_____

_____

_____

_____

c.  Would you want to be the real you every day? If so, why or why not?

_____

_____

_____

_____

_____

_____

_____

_____

_____

_____

_____

Note: Who are you, humbly and unapologetically? Be proud of who you truly are.

6. What sacrifices have you made to make sure you stay on task to get the life you deserve?

_____

_____

_____

_____

_____

_____

_____

_____

E.g.: When my ex-husband and I separated, I rented out a room from my friend for $600.00 a month. When my ex got my car repossessed, I decided not to get a car in order to avoid spending my money on a car payment and car insurance. I took Uber pool or Lyft shared to work. I worked 3 nights a week, 12-16 hours per shift, and wisely decided the places I would go out for social events. All the money I was saving was for my investment in real estate and the development and start-up of Peace Under Pressure, Corporation. I knew that the outcome would be greater than my sacrifice.

_____

_____

_____

_____

_____

_____

_____

_____

_____

Note: Be careful of secluding yourself on your journey to finding your peace under the pressures of life. Don't nudge others out or refuse constructive criticism. Having peace under pressure entails surrendering your heart. Be sure to use discernment to know to whom to surrender yourself. This allows you to form the best relationships while building and becoming the best and strongest version of yourself. Remember life is all about love, love for oneself, and love for others. This is the perfect recipe for building beneficial, long-lasting relationships, helping others also level up into their best character.

Note: When I decided to start peace under pressure, Corporation. I had to trust that my friends and family members would support me—whether that meant being on the board, donating money, or just being my cheerleaders. No woman is an island. Alternatively, even if people could not be there for me in any of the capacities that I expected them to be, I had to be okay with their honesty in communicating that with me. Becoming the best version of yourself is being willing to be flexible, being understanding, and seeking knowledge.

Note: Where you end up in your career does not have to be determined by your past or current circumstances.

Note: The pressure of life does not stop because you decided to focus on the most important journey you will ever take for yourself. Remember Peace Under Pressure, Corporation. is your safe place to take this journey, knowing you will be triumphant regardless of what transpired in your past and what might be transpiring in your present. Utilize Peace Under Pressure, Corporation. for all the resources it has to offer. The discussion groups, therapy, mental and physical wellness activities, as well as networking.  So please make sure you are striving for peace because life will provide you with pressure.

7. Do you find yourself daydreaming about a life that seems like yours, yet so different from your current life? I encourage you to focus on that dream and meditate on it. Try to manifest this dream into reality. Believe it is yours. Remember imagination can manifest into reality. Write down your dream and speak it into existence and work toward your daily goals!

_____

_____

_____

_____

_____

_____

_____

_____

_____

_____

_____

8. How much time you put into something shows its level of importance in your life. Are you using your time on something

that will bring about the manifestation of your personal growth?  If so, please explain what that thing is.

_____

_____

_____

_____

_____

_____

_____

_____

_____

a.      To which person, place, or thing do you give attention that is a distraction from obtaining the best version of yourself?

_____

_____

_____

_____

_____

_____

_____

_____

_____

_____

9. Are you wasting time doing something that is not helping you grow, learn, and become the best version of yourself for yourself? What are you wasting your time on? Watching TV, going out with friends or family, talking on the phone/texting, social media? What are some things you can do to shift your focus?

_____

_____

_____

_____

_____

_____

_____

_____

10. Focusing your energy takes time and discipline. Are you committed to fighting for the journey to your purpose? What does this fight entail you doing daily to reach your goal? Please write a list of 5 things you can do every day to help you get closer to finding your purpose.

1. _____

_____

2. _____

_____

3. _____

_____

4. _____

_____

5. _____

_____

6. _____

_____

# Let's Measure Your Self-Esteem

Date: _____

On a scale from 0 to 5, with 0 being not at all and 5 being very much, rate how you currently feel in the following categories.

Confident

0          1          2          3          4          5

Happy

0          1          2          3          4          5

Sad

0          1          2          3          4          5

Disgusted

0          1          2          3          4          5

Overwhelmed

0          1          2          3          4          5

Alone

0        1        2        3        4        5

Loved

0        1        2        3        4        5

Liked

0        1        2        3        4        5

Attractive

0        1        2        3        4        5

# Week 11: The Ultimate Sacrifice

1.  What kinds of things are helping you stay committed to the process? What do you need to help you stay focused or become more focused than you already are?

_____

_____

_____

_____

_____

_____

_____

_____

_____

2.  Never give anyone or anything your power by allowing it to steal your joy. You have every right to be happy and at peace. What can you start reciting or referencing when you encounter

a situation that may or may not be out of your control and has turned for the worst?

_____

_____

_____

_____

_____

_____

_____

_____

_____

3. All work and no play is never the best way to accomplish your goals. What are some things you can do in moderation to still be able to enjoy life with family and friends?

_____

_____

_____

_____

_____

_____

_____

_____

_____

_____

4. Do you need help with time management?

_____

_____

_____

_____

_____

_____

_____

_____

_____

_____

Note: Sometimes you can break for half the amount of time that you worked. For example, if you read and did research for 6 hours, take a 3-hour break. Do not be hard on yourself if the times are not exact. Self-discipline is the key to success. However, being flexible is also crucial. Having a daily/weekly/monthly schedule helps you to stay on task. Always give yourself a one-day break out of a 7-day week, to do something that you enjoy. Mental health is very important on your journey to walking in your light and finding your purpose. "At the point in life where your talents meet the needs of the world is where God wants you to be." -Albert Schweitzer[5]

5. For the sake of developing your character, what are you willing to give up that is a distraction, so that you will find the time to pursue becoming the best version of yourself, no matter how uncomfortable it makes you?

_____

_____

_____

_____

_____

_____

_____

_____

_____

_____

E.g.: I have decided not to purchase a car or have my own house or apartment to save money to build a business and invest in real estate.

6. Are you willing to start sacrificing some things to have a more bountiful life?

_____

_____

_____

_____

_____

_____

_____

_____

a.      Are you willing to decrease your weekly/monthly allowance to save more money per/month?

_____

_____

_____

_____

_____

_____

_____

_____

_____

b.      Are you willing to shop for Items that you need and not want (treating yourself once in a while)?

_____

_____

_____

_____

_____

_____

_____

_____

_____

_____

c.      Are you willing to create a check and balance system to track your money coming in and going out?

_____

_____

_____

_____

_____

_____

_____

_____

_____

d.     Are you willing to shop for items on sale?

_____

_____

_____

_____

_____

_____

_____

_____

_____

e.     Are you willing to use coupons?

_____

_____

_____

_____

_____

f.   Are you willing to maintain a lifestyle below your income?

g.  If your answer is no, write down a list of reasons why starting
    now is not possible.

    1._____

    _____

    2._____

    _____

    3._____

    _____

    4._____

    _____

    5._____

    _____

h.  Once you have written your list of reasons why starting now is a
    problem, explain why each reason is more of a priority than
    focusing on yourself at this time.

    1._____

    _____

2._____

_____

3._____

_____

4._____

_____

5._____

_____

7.  If you could have more power over something you considered a character flaw, what would you have power over? How would you use that power to build up your character?

_____

_____

_____

_____

_____

_____

_____

_____

_____

_____

E.g.: I wish I had more power over whom I trusted with intimate, personal information. People would turn around and use my vulnerabilities as weapons against me. I am currently working on having more discernment over who I share information with.

8.  In this workbook, many questions pertain to the building of one's character. Why do you think these inquiries are important in aiding the development of your character on your journey?

_____

_____

_____

_____

_____

_____

_____

_____

_____

9. Are you complacent? Explain your answer.

_____

_____

_____

_____

_____

_____

_____

_____

_____

a.    Have you lost your drive to want more out of life? Are you just existing here on earth or are you living and taking advantage of life?

_____

_____

_____

_____

_____

_____

_____

_____

_____

_____

_____

_____

_____

10. Like all muscles, the brain must be exercised over some time to develop the necessary skills to develop strength. What skills would you like to develop to help build your character to become a better person?

_____

_____

_____

_____

_____

_____

_____

_____

_____

_____

E.g.: I would like to develop more patience. I believe I have been hasty in making some decisions in my life, resulting in me wondering how things would have turned out if I had taken more time to think about the results.

Note: There is nothing that says you will not experience problems in your life.

Note: I work night shift 3-4 nights a week for 12-16 hours each shift. My circadian rhythm or sleep/wake cycle is off. Sometimes I only get 4-6 hours of sleep a day. But when there is an open window to read or research how to develop Peace Under

Pressure, Corporation. I make the sacrifice to read and do as much research as possible during that period.

Note: As a recently divorced woman, I am still working through all of the things that I have been through. I am not healed. I am healing. I have just chosen not to let any of my past hurts or pain stop me from obtaining the things I want out of life. I believe that all members of Peace under Pressure are capable of the same things. I am progressing every day. I also need all of the activities Peace Under Pressure has to offer to continue to build my character.

Note: "Fill your life with Women that empower you, that help you believe in your magic and aid them to believe in their exceptional power and their incredible magic too. Women that believe in each other can survive anything. Women who believe in each other create army's that will win kingdoms and wars." - Nikita Gill[6]

Note: Fear and rejection are not easy emotions to deal with. Often, they cause us to feel like we are not good enough and cause feelings of loneliness. This is very far from the truth. You are not alone (Even if you think you are, here in this organization you are no longer alone). Look at you living. It might not feel so great all of the time, but here you are, breathing, eating, smelling, and tasting. Now, because of what happened to you, you learned something about yourself that you may not have known before.

11. Write down something you thought/think was a tragedy that you turned into triumph.  If you do not have anything triumphant to write about, I challenge you to force yourself to think of something positive that came out of your situation that may have changed you for the better.

_____

_____

_____

_____

_____

_____

_____

_____

_____

_____

_____

_____

E.g.: From my experience, I have learned to forgive and not hold a grudge against people. I never take anything personally. However, I do hold people accountable for their actions. What I do now is focus on moving forward in my life and work on the things that matter the most because I know that I am in control of my happiness. Are you still holding a grudge?

---

_____

_____

_____

_____

_____

_____

_____

_____

_____

_____

_____

a.      Write down why that triumph was so important, and what you learned about yourself.

_____

_____

_____

_____

_____

_____

_____

_____

_____

_____

Note: Because I care so much about creating Peace Under Pressure, Corporation. being honest in my personal journey is necessary for the development of myself and all of our members. This is all in honesty.  As of March 5, 2019, I have not come to the point in my life where I have forgiven my ex-husband. I am working on it and hope to someday be able to do so. I know that it's necessary for the progression of my character and personal development so that I can accomplish all the things I want. I tell you all the truth because I want everyone to know that I too am working on becoming the best version of myself, and I also need help doing so.

Note: Being the 100% pure, carefree, fun, honest and loving person you are is not an easy feat, especially after what has happened to you. Fear, rejection, and loss can sometimes make allowing another person to get close to you seem impossible. I would like to ask you to take that fear and turn it into a learned experience and use discernment when meeting new people.

Note: Peacemaking is not appeasement! Many times in my marriage I forgave my ex-husband for the hurt he was causing me. My biggest mistake was not with forgiveness, but my decision to trust him too soon after each wrongdoing. I knew trust and forgiveness are two different things. However, I did not treat them as such. I never allowed him to show me he deserved to be trusted after he hurt me. Thus, he had no reason to change.

12. Have you ever used two concepts interchangeably? If so, what? Explain your answer.

_____

_____

_____

_____

_____

_____

_____

_____

a.  What are two nouns or verbs that you used interchangeably in your relationship that had nothing to do with each other, but were used out of the convenience of peace?

_____

_____

_____

_____

_____

_____

_____

_____

_____

_____

_____

13. Did the person you were with omit information but say they
    were not lying? Please explain the situation. How can you use
    discernment to make sure this doesn't happen to you again?

_____

_____

_____

_____

_____

_____

_____

_____

# Let's Measure Your Self-Esteem

Date: _____

On a scale from 0 to 5, with 0 being not at all and 5 being very much, rate how you currently feel in the following categories.

Confident

0          1          2          3          4          5

Happy

0          1          2          3          4          5

Sad

0          1          2          3          4          5

Disgusted

0          1          2          3          4          5

Overwhelmed

0          1          2          3          4          5

Alone

0     1     2     3     4     5

Loved

0     1     2     3     4     5

Liked

0     1     2     3     4     5

Attractive

0     1     2     3     4     5

# Week 12: Out with the Old and In with the New

1.  "Longing for the ideal while criticizing the real is evidence of immaturity. On the other hand, settling for the real without striving for the ideal is complacency. Maturity is living with the tension." *A Purpose Driven Life* - Rick Warren[7]

    How does this quote from Rick Warren fit into your life at this moment?

    _____

    _____

    _____

    _____

    _____

    _____

    _____

    _____

    _____

2. Dedicating your life to something that makes you feel a sense of joy is an essential step toward finding your purpose. What is something you are willing to commit to that will help towards your character development?

_____

_____

_____

_____

_____

_____

_____

_____

_____

a. What old routines are you willing to let go of that don't allow you to make progress in your life?

_____

_____

_____

_____

_____

_____

_____

_____

_____

_____

_____

b.     What new habits are you willing and ready to accept?

_____

_____

_____

_____

_____

_____

_____

_____

_____

c.     Are you ready to change the way you currently think about yourself to become the best version of yourself?

_____

_____

_____

_____

_____

_____

_____

_____

_____

_____

3.  If fear comes to mind while answering any of the above
    questions, what are they? List them all and be very detailed.

    _____

    _____

    _____

    _____

    _____

    _____

    _____

    _____

    _____

4.  What would happen if you still worked on committing yourself
    to things that gave you joy, while this feeling of fear was upon
    you?

    _____

    _____

    _____

    _____

_____

_____

_____

_____

_____

_____

_____

(Proverbs 4:23 GNT) "Be Careful how you think; your life is shaped by your thoughts."

"No matter where you go, there you are."- Buckaroo Banzai[8]
...so why not be as beautiful as you can be while you're there?

NOTE: A commitment to being rich or famous is a very broad commitment. Try to make it as specific as possible. E.g.: I want to write a children's book, I want to open a daycare, I want to start an online boutique, and I want to own a few rental properties.

5.  What are the differences between worry and meditation?

_____

_____

_____

_____

_____

_____

_____

_____

_____

a.    How is one detrimental to your character development?

_____

_____

_____

_____

_____

_____

_____

_____

b.   How is the other beneficial towards your character
     development?

_____

_____

_____

_____

_____

_____

_____

_____

_____

6.   How can you use meditation to shift any worries you may have?

_____

_____

_____

_____

_____

_____

_____

_____

_____

_____

7. If something unpleasant has occurred in your life, whether today or some time in your past, try not to blame yourself. Instead, ask yourself, "What can I learn from this situation?" What did you learn from your most recent unpleasant encounter?

_____

_____

_____

_____

_____

_____

_____

_____

_____

_____

8. Smile! A smile can change your whole perspective on your day. Even when times are not the best, a smile can help reduce stress levels. What do you have going on in your life that you can be happy and smile about? Write a list. This list can help you in your moments of need, sadness, stress, or difficulty.

1. _____

_____

2. _____

_____

3. _____

_____

4. _____

_____

5. _____

_____

Note: It may seem hard to think of something to make you smile, but even if you can't think of anything to make you smile, make the choice right now to smile anyway. Then, at that very moment, you will have something to smile about. You challenged yourself to handle life differently and more positively. Don't wait for anyone or anything to bring you joy or happiness. Joy and happiness are yours to bring unto yourself. Smile!

Note: I want all of the members to come out of this program motivated to do better, be better, and be able to teach others how to do the same thing. One of my favorite authors, Rick Warren, makes it very clear in his book *The Purpose Driven Life*, "Your circumstances are temporary, but your character will last forever."[9] He also says, "To change your life, you must change the way you think. Behind everything you do is a thought...[10] The way you think determines the way you feel, and the way you feel influences the way you act."[11]

9. We are all trying to do well, but life offers up many temptations. What are your temptations?

_____

_____

_____

_____

_____

_____

_____

_____

_____

_____

a.   What are some temptations that might come up that may work
     against character building? These temptations may come about
     when you're lonely, bored, depressed, stressed, tired, hurt,
     angry, worried, sad, doubtful....

_____

_____

_____

_____

_____

_____

_____

_____

b.   What alternatives are there to falling into your temptation? E.g.:
     Do more work, start a new project, relax, take a break, refocus
     your attention on positive things that bring joy and inspire you.

The more you focus your attention on negativity, the more negativity controls your thoughts and takes hold of you and your emotions, giving negativity power over you. Explain what thought comes to mind when reading this.

_____

_____

_____

_____

_____

_____

_____

_____

_____

_____

_____

Note: Sometimes your circumstances may not be something you can change or control. However, you can control how you handle your attitude towards the situation.

10. Dictionary.com defines "PRIDE" as a feeling of being better than others." Do not let pride get in the way of your character development. We are all trying to make progress in becoming the best versions of ourselves.

_____

_____

_____

_____

_____

_____

_____

_____

a.   Have you let pride get in the way of your personal development? Why?

_____

_____

_____

_____

_____

_____

_____

_____

_____

_____

_____

b.    How can you allow yourself to prevent pride from being a driving force in your life?

_____

_____

_____

_____

_____

_____

_____

_____

_____

# Let's Measure Your Self-Esteem

Date: _____

On a scale from 0 to 5, with 0 being not at all and 5 being very much, rate how you currently feel in the following categories.

Confident

0        1        2        3        4        5

Happy

0        1        2        3        4        5

Sad

0        1        2        3        4        5

Disgusted

0        1        2        3        4        5

Overwhelmed

0        1        2        3        4        5

Alone

0     1     2     3     4     5

Loved

0     1     2     3     4     5

Liked

0     1     2     3     4     5

Attractive

0     1     2     3     4     5

# Week 13: Stay the Course

1.  At this point, I would have hoped that many of you have participated in several activities that were suggested through Peace Under Pressure, Corporation. or a few things that may have been recommended to you by a family member or friend. Have any of those activities made you feel enthusiastic about doing it again? If so, what activity is it?

_____

_____

_____

_____

_____

_____

_____

_____

_____

_____

_____

2. If nothing at this point makes you feel enthusiastic, write a list of things or activities you have always wanted to do. Do not let age be a limitation. It is essential that you try different activities. If you don't like it, it was only an experiment and not a failure. So, try something else, no matter how old you are. You are as old as you feel, and experimenting is how you discover yourself.

_____

_____

_____

_____

_____

_____

_____

_____

_____

_____

_____

_____

_____

3. Did you find yourself comparing your journey to other members? If so, why do you find it hard to stay focused on the steps you are taking personally for your personal growth?

_____

_____

_____

_____

_____

_____

_____

_____

_____

Note: When you find yourself comparing yourself to others, shift your thoughts. Focus on what you can do and what you want to do better. Through this process I urge you not to compare yourself to others. It is bound to fill you with pride which stunts productivity or can build insecurities that will discourage you and stunt your productivity. Neither is good for character development. You are your own competition. Run your own race.

4. Sometimes we have jobs we love, sometimes we have jobs we dislike. In all cases, think about all the wonderful things that your current job allows you to acquire. List the things you can obtain and the life you can afford because of the job you have.

_____

_____

_____

_____

_____

_____

_____

_____

_____

_____

E.g. When I stopped allowing my job to steal my joy, I started to look at my job as a bank that provided me resources without interest or penalties. Because of my job I was able to invest in myself and the life I want to live. I grew to appreciate my job and what it was doing for me. Therefore, I became more productive, started doing things with a great attitude, and became very happy. I stopped complaining about work altogether.

Note: Be sure to develop a positive attitude in all that you do. It's the pathway to reaping the results of what you sow.

5. The road to your destination can be exciting, and yet trying at times. Either way, it is your journey. How are you living on your journey to your destination?

_____

_____

_____

_____

_____

_____

_____

_____

_____

_____

_____

a.     Is your journey filled with friends and loved ones who are
       encouraging and motivating? How are the people in your life
       contributing to your journey?

_____

_____

_____

_____

_____

_____

_____

_____

_____

_____

_____

_____

6. What has life taught you? What can you teach others about what you have learned?

_____

_____

_____

_____

_____

_____

_____

_____

_____

_____

_____

_____

Note: Never overlook what's occurring in your life while on your journey. Whatever is happening is building you to become the person you were meant to be. Just slow down and enjoy the moments with friends and family. Take that walk, sit by the pool, play with your kids. Life is a beautiful thing and has so much to offer! Work hard, play harder! But always remember to stay balanced and keep things in perspective. Don't take anything or anyone for granted, and always be grateful. Never Give up. You are in this! Look at you doing this!

7. If life throws a curve ball into your journey of building yourself up, what perspective will you choose to deal with the circumstance?

_____

_____

_____

_____

_____

_____

_____

_____

_____

_____

a.      What is a perspective that feels wrong?

_____

_____

_____

_____

_____

_____

_____

_____

b.      What is a perspective that feels right?

_____

_____

_____

_____

_____

_____

_____

_____

_____

_____

_____

8. What's going to help you build your character in life? e.g.:
   Starting a business, mentoring, volunteering?

_____

_____

_____

_____

_____

_____

_____

_____

_____

Note: Don't expect anyone else to care more about you having peace under the pressures of life than you do. Remember, "Love yourself. You are the most important person in your life."[12]- Araceli M. Ream. So, what do you intend on doing with this gift called life?

Note: Stress, trauma, fear causes the production of cortisol and Adrenaline to give a fright or flight response. The same stress response kicks in when you re-live or remember a moment in time that caused you trouble, fear, or anxiety.

Note: "Worry" in Webster's dictionary: "give way to anxiety or unease; allow one's mind to dwell on difficulty or troubles." Worry can produce cortisol and adrenaline. The same reaction occurs regardless of whether the danger is real or imagined. What does all this mean in real life? It means that what you remember or imagine is *actually* happening, as far as your brain is concerned.

Note: Mediation, on the other hand can be the aim of focusing on positive things. Focusing on positive things may trigger the release of endorphins, increasing dopamine, serotonin, and melatonin. This cocktail of chemicals flooding the bloodstream leaves the meditator feeling calm and happy.

9. Are you going to spend your time today worrying or meditating? What can you meditate about to induce feeling calm and happy? We all have something to be grateful for. Use that thought to break through to all that you deserve.

_____

_____

_____

_____

_____

_____

_____

_____

_____

_____

_____

_____

10. If you have a habit of always being grateful for what you do have, you won't have the time to complain about what you don't have. Complaining also delays better days. Today, what are you grateful for?

_____

_____

_____

_____

_____

_____

_____

_____

_____

_____

Note: Don't let anyone confuse you with mental or emotional abuse or manipulation, only confirm your thoughts or feelings through discernment. I convinced myself that I was in a loving marriage with someone who was far from perfect. Without the help of him telling me that I was ungrateful, or that I could not love him right, I might have been able to see that I was being emotionally abused and manipulated.

(1 John 4:18) "There is no fear in love; perfect love drives out all fear."

# Let's Measure Your Self-Esteem

Date: _____

On a scale from 0 to 5, with 0 being not at all and 5 being very much, rate how you currently feel in the following categories.

Confident

0        1        2        3        4        5


Happy

0        1        2        3        4        5


Sad

0        1        2        3        4        5


Disgusted

0        1        2        3        4        5


Overwhelmed

0        1        2        3        4        5

Alone

0          1          2          3          4          5

Loved

0          1          2          3          4          5

Liked

0          1          2          3          4          5

Attractive

0          1          2          3          4          5

## Afterword

I have been walking and working in my purpose for a short period of time. It feels good every day to get up to do the thing that I love no matter how hard it gets. In my analysis of fear, in hindsight leaving earth before I got a chance to accomplish all the things that I needed or wanted to, to feel accomplished in life was what scared me. Having discovered my purpose, I am happy. Happiness to me, is working and walking in my purpose no matter how difficult things may get. So, walk in your purpose, so you can be happy too.

I hope the questions asked, as well as the notes and examples provided in this workbook help you to gain the momentum you need to establish peace under the pressures of life. Keep this workbook. Every time you reach a new level of growth and level up your character development, this workbook will help keep things on task when difficult times come and you need a reminder that you are capable of anything you put your mind to. THINK BIG!

## Nemadia B. Knuckles

# Endnotes

1. Warren, Rick. "Cultivating Community." The Purpose Driven Life." Zondervan, Grand Rapids, Michigan 49530, 2002.pp149

2. Graham, Billy. The Holy Spirit: Activating God's Power in your life. W Published Group. (1978). p92.

3. Chernoff Mark, Chenoff Angle (MarcandAngle) "Never regret being a good person, to the wrong people. Your behavior says everything about you, and their behavior says everything about them." Feb, 2017 8:23pm. Tweet.

4. Maraboli, Steve, Stevemaraboli.net.Bettertoday, 7 May 2013: https://stevemaraboli.net/your-history-your-destiny/

5. Abrams,Rhonda. "Social Responsibility & Sustainability." Successful Business Plan Secrets &, Strategies, PlanningShop™, 2014, 6th Edition, pp254

6. Gill, Nikita. "MeanwhilePoetry." Monday, 27 May. https://meanwhilepoetry.tumblr.com/post/168398720128/fill-your-life-with-women-that-empower-you-that

7. Warren, Rick. "Protect Your Church." The Purpose Driven Life." Zondervan, Grand Rapids, Michigan 49530, 2002. pp162

8. The Adventures of Buckaroo Banzai Across the 8th Dimension. Dir. W.D. Richter, Neil Canton. Perf. Peter Weller, John Lithgow, Ellen Barkin, Jeff Goldlum, Christopher LLoyd, Clancy Brown. 1984. 20th Century Fox. unknown copywrite year. DVD

9. Warren, Rick. "Transformed by Trouble." The Purpose Driven Life." Zondervan, Grand Rapids, Michigan 49530, 2002. pp197

10. Warren, Rick. "How We Grow." The Purpose Driven Life." Zondervan, Grand Rapids, Michigan 49530,2002 .pp 181

11. Warren, Rick. "How We Grow." The Purpose Driven Life." Zondervan, Grand Rapids, Michigan 49530,2002.pp182

12. Ream M, Araceli, growintowings. "love yourself. You are the most important person in your life." Instagram, 20 Dec 2016, https://www.instagram.com/p/BOPzlRdgdaC/?utm_source=ig_web_button_share_sheet

Peace Under Pressure Self Discovery Workbook provides information on enhancing your analytical skills. The workbook will help you decide what works best for you when making decisions for your life, and your mental health and wellness. You will learn how you physically act out when dealing with emotional triggers and be able to make rational choices for yourself when making decisions for the greatest return in the value of your life. You will learn to forgive yourself and the power of discernment to live a purpose-driven life. You will learn the importance of setting expectations for oneself and get an understanding of who you are. You will practice setting limitations for yourself and others for overall comfort, and fight for confidence through self-preservation. You will see how I took a life-changing event and made it into a pathway of turning tragedy into triumph.

This book is endorsed by : Kiara Moore, M.A., L.P.C.M.H. she is a Licensed Mental Health Therapist with several years of experience working with various diagnoses. Kiara received her Undergraduate Degree in Psychology from the West Chester University of Pennsylvania and her Graduate Degree from the Eastern University of Pennsylvania in Clinical/Counseling Psychology. Kiara Moore was certified as a Grief Recovery Specialist® through the Grief Recovery Institute® in 2013.~ Kiara Moore Therapeutic Services offers a variety of counseling services including:
Virtual Counseling, Individual Counseling, Marriage/Couples Counseling, Family Counseling, Grief Recovery (group/individual), Professional Workshops and Seminars.

Nemadia B. Knuckles is the Founder and Executive Director of Peace Under Pressure, Corporation. She is also a licensed Respiratory Care Practitioner at a level 1 trauma center. She survived a bitter divorce and was able to discover self-love with the help of close family, friends, books, and physical and nonphysical activities.

She thought to share the support she received with women in life-altering events so that they may also see the beauty that lies within. Nemadia graduated with a B.A. in Liberal Studies with a concentration In Psychology, Sociology, and Secondary Education.

Made in the USA
Middletown, DE
28 June 2020